Also by Daisy de Villeneuve,
He Said, She Said

Daisy de Villeneuve
I Told You So

Foreword by Zac Posen

POCKO

For Joe

I Told You So

© 2003 Daisy de Villeneuve and
   Pocko Editions

Design by Olga Norman
Edited by Nicola Schwartz and Inigo Asís

Published by Pocko Editions
51 3rd Avenue
London W10 4XR
T: +44 (0) 208 964 9580
info@pocko.com

Printed in Italy

ISBN 1-903977-19-3

Thank You to:
The Pocko Family, Lucien Rothenstein,
Ronnie Cooke Newhouse and Topshop!
Maurizio Brivio and Larissa Soffientini,
Marc Hulson, Michael Baigent, PJQT,
Zac Posen, Christopher Kangis, plus
friends and family for all their support.

This book has been kindly supported by:

TOPSHOP

www.pocko.com

Foreword

Daisy de Villeneuve is a truly
remarkable artist who has a gift
for translating the pathos of her
daily adventures into smart, mod-
ern, and comic work. This book
explores the feline side of other
women and how the laws of the
"love jungle" have entered into
the "cosmopolitan kingdom".

So, enjoy this marvelous book,
and make sure you read carefully
and take notes, for you never
know when these rules may apply
to you.

Love,
Zac Posen

Introduction

I Told You So, is a series of short stories about different girls. What they all share in common is that they are the same type: 'Bitch'. These girls have somehow ended up entangled in my life and this story follows my encounters with them: always showing up at the wrong time, being rude to my friends, stealing my men and taking what they can from me. All in the name of innocence? And then they end up turning it all around and making me feel guilty.

'It was fascinating how men would fall for her. With her small town vibe and naivety, they wanted to show her the world, be her guide, make her a star. She would pull tantrums all the time, run off, act like a total brat. Every time the guy was lured back in, she had the power, she was psychotic, twisted, badly behaved, but it was if he was oblivious to all of this. She's the kind of girl that has a big mouth and an opinion, a typically clueless opinion.'

Girls dread girls like this.

Daisy de Villenueve

She somehow gets your telephone number and starts
calling non-stop, especially
at the wrong time. There's
always a drama, she doesn't
quite comprehend that not
only is she a total maniac,
but that maybe you have
things to do other than
listen to her whiny voice.

It8 It's not something to
search out, I've just stumb-
led across it a few times.

She's normally a friend of
a friend, or you work with
her, or went to school with
her, or she's a friend of the
family or you live with her,
or god forbid she's a relat-
ive. It's not like there's
always an out. It's kind of
about the circumstances you
encounter.

She She tracked me down at
work, I didn't even like this

person, why was she calling
me? Can't she sense that I

don't like her? Doesn't

she realise that I think
she's a x clingy wet-drip.
Back off!

I hadn't seen her in two yea
years. I had been living
abroad. She would wri write
to me every few months. I
wasn't planning on seeing
her, but she called me and
we were in the same city. I
decided to see her, as it
had been a couple of years,
thinking that maybe she had
changed. When I met up with
her she did seem quite
mature, sk so I kind ed of
brushed the past aside and
started spending time with
her. Big mistake!

She mentioned how her friend
had slept with him, which
happened to coincide with
when I had slept with him.
She told me this information
a year after ~~thw~~ the event.
I wondered why she told me
this as she knew I had slept
with him and, if it was true
that her friend had as well
during the same time, why
was she telling me? It wasn't
like I was involved with him
It was like some exclusive
 gossip that only she knew
about. Also, why tell me a
year later? Uh, what was the
point? You can be discreet
about these things and if
she hadn't mentioned it I
wouldn't have known. Even
though it had ~~beeb~~ been
a while, a year, it really
didn't make me feel great
to hear this.

One te time she came over to
my house and within minutes
she was trying on my shoes,
looking through my clothes
and using my make up. Plus
she wanted to borrow money.

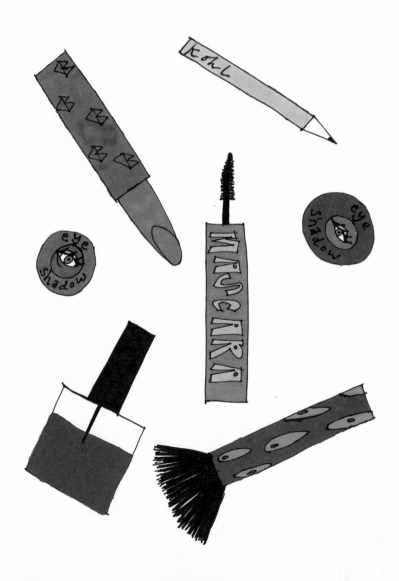

I asked her if she knew him.
I thought she probably would
know him, as they had a mutual
friend in common. I told her
I had been going out with him
for a couple months. She
responded with, "Are you sure?

I'm really good friends with
him and he's never mentioned
a girl or girlfriend". I
must have sounded quite shock-
ed at this information, as
she started to back track
saying that she wasn't
actually that good friends
with him.

She was completely annoying,
getting on my nerves,
complaining and whining.

She was sucking all the ~~ener~~
energy out from me. I end
up thinking that I should

be nice to her. She's like
a pest. I find her selfish
and the only reason she

attempts at a friendship

with me is because ~~e~~she

wants something.

I observed how guys would
act ari around her, the more
badly behaved she was the
more they liked her. She
could be a total bitch to
her girl friends right in
front of any man and he
would still think she was
the sweetest thing on earth.

Wearing her big fake Fendi
 sunglasses she'd say in a
baby voice, "I don't have
any money for the train",
and he would reach into
his pocket and give her
some cash.

We met up for tea after the
Summer holidays, she starts
bragging to me about how she
slept with this guy that she
knew I really fancied. I

thought if I had slept with
someone that she really
fancied, she'd be the last
person I'd tell.

I already had a friend over
at my house, when my next
visitor came by. They knew

each ~~othef~~ other, but not
well. "What's she doing

~~hee~~ here?" my friend asked.

There was an uncomfortable
vibe and my visitor left.

There was no need for my

friend to be so rude.

" You have to meet this guy,
you'll really like him," she
says. I meet him and think
he's cute, we all go back to
his house. She's running
around the house with a
camera. I'm lying on the
guy's bed with him. She
looks through the door and

goes "Oooeoooohhhhhh".

Something happens and he

gets up, she corners him
and he spends the rest of
the night with her. I leave
early in the morning. I
ask her if she slept with
him? She says "No comment".

She phoned me up and started
talking about her, e̶b̶ even
knowing that she was a good
friend of mine said, ' I
really don't like that girl'.

When I walked into the room
she was wearing jeans like
mine and had done her eye-

liner like how I do mine.

Freaky Friday, I knew I

shouldn't have told her
where I bought my clothes.

She's always asking a
million questions; Where
are you going? What are you
doing? Who invited you? Why
did they invite you? Who's

going to be there? Maybe
you'll meet someone? Do
you think He's going to be
there? What are you going
to wear? What time do you
have to be there? Do you
think there'll be food
there? What do you think
you'll have to drink?
Maybe you'll go home with
someone? Do you think you'll
go home with someone? I
bet you do go home with
someone!
   Oh, you're so lucky
you're going out and you're
gonna meet the one.

Wish I was you.

The guy that I had been
seeing she was now dating.
It bothered me so much, her
subtle way of telling me how
great things were between
them. I guess what really
pissed me off was that she
was still in my life. Even
when she was 3,000 miles
awag away. She had to
creep back in! Whenever
she called me she was like,
"hiiiiii".

I first met her for like
five minutes at a trendy shop
opening. When I met her this
time she was super friendly
verging on totally fake,
acting like my new best
friend. I later found out
that she had bitched about
me to a bunch of people,
including an old friend
(he was the one that told
me), but he £ didn't tell
me absolutely everything
she had said so as to not
upset me. But what he did
tell me I believed. I
~~belieb belived him because~~
believed him because when
she did talk to me for
those five minutes when we
first met she bitched about
other people I knew, and
some I didn't know but had
heard of. She badmouthed
them terribly.
  As for what I thought of
her, well, I think she's
too fat to wear midriff
tops but I'm keeping my
opinions to myself.
  What goes around comes
around.

She phoned me up to tell me
that she had bumped into him
in the street. According to

her, he had asked about me
and mentioned he'd like to
see me. Apparently he ~~said~~
asked her if he should call
me? She told him not to
bother calling me. She knew

perfectly well that I wanted
to see him.

I felt guilty for not liking
her. I was wanted to kill the
person that had given her my
telephone number. She called
me up and asked if I wanted
to go get some dinner. I
felt sorry for her and,
unfortunately, agreed to
join her for food, thinking
maybe she's okay; it's only
that I get that kind of a
needy vibe from her. Over
dinner she complained

about her love life. I
must have been bored and I
told her too much about

mine, so after that she'd
call sporadically,ranting
on about her "I HATE MEN"
attitude and feeling that
we were united in having
something in common, except
she had projected that onto
me. I never said I shared
her opinions. I needed to
get as far away from her
as possible.

She once phoned me up while
I was living in Paris, to
ask if she could come stay
with me and bring her cat. I
lived alone and I didn't
want her or her cat to
bombard me. From that telephone converstation her
last words were, "will you
support me?" I wasn't sure
if she meant emotionally
or financially. With her
wild child antics, I just
didn't want to know.

She calls about Ipm and
he's still in my bed. She
says to me, "Did you kiss

him?" "Yes" I reply. "What

else?" she says "You know..."
I say. "Is he there?" she
says. "Yes" I say. "How
could you! I liked him"

(this is coming from someone that has a boyfriend).
Anyway you couldn't have

had sex with him because
you have your period. I'm

putting the phone down".

she says.

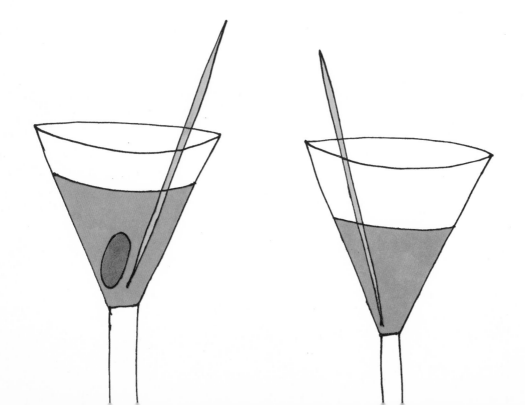

We go out for drinks and she
proceeds to tell me that she

doesn't think he's for me,
that he probably won't call
me and that she can't see

the appeal.

Her make-up was all messed up,
it kept getting in her eyes.
"Don't rub your eyes" I said.
Once we were outside and had
walked ten minutes, she
would turn to me and say, "I
need to re-do my make-up".
After three attempts of her
coming and going back to the
house.I should have figured,
if this was annoying at the
beginning... just imagine
how the evening would end!

One time she was at my house
and we were talking about
this guy that we both knew,
then all of a sudden she's
like, "my friend's going
out with him". I had been
seeing him too but he had

been in New York for a

couple months; I had to hold

back my tears. When I

confronted him he said,
"yes, I do have a new girl-

friend". Then said- he said

in regard to us, "we weren't
really a couple. We were
just friends that had sex".

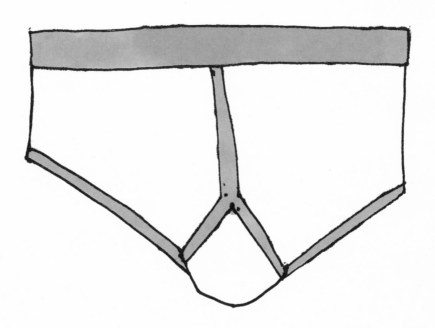

She'll **find** your weak spots
and start digging.

One day I went over to her
house and she didn't say
that much. She stormed out,
I asked her boyfriend, ꝯ
"what's wrong with her?"
"She thinks you're being a
 bitch" he said. "Why?" I
said. "I don't know, You
ask her?" he said. I
called her when I got
home. Her boyfriend answered, "Can I speak to her?"
I said. "She doesn't want
to talk to you" he said.
"Why?" I said. "she thinks
you're being a bitch".
"Why does she think I'm
being a bitch? What did I
do?" I said. "Ask her" he
said. "How can I ask her if
she doesn't want to talk to
me?" I said. I called back
the next day, the boyfriend
answered, same reply.

She'll call and I'll d̶ say
that ̶1̶8̶- I'm in a meeting
or really busy. "Can I call
you back?" I'm trying to get
out of talking to her. I am

truly busy but I'm reminded
of the excuses guys use on
me all the time like the all
too familiar one, "I'll call
you later!" When they never
call, I end up not making
any plans with people just
in case they ̶v̶ call, but
they don't and I end up
getting totally stressed
out. So I ̶k̶e̶ keep this in
mind and tell myself I'll
call her back in a few days.

I felt like it was like high-
school, all these girls being
so ridiculous about this guy;
I just didn't want to hear
about it. It was childish
behaviour, it was all too
incestuous.

There she was...the other
girl. The one he decided to
be with. I had told him I'd
be back in a month but what
does he do? Gw Get a new
girl. I never saw them
together but I always
wondered what she knew
about us. Even though he's
not with her anymore,
whenever I see her out I
still think "so she was the
girl". I couldn't figure
out what he saw in her, I
was jealous and I felt sad
he had chosen her over me.

I caught them kissing in
the toilets, my best friend
and my date.

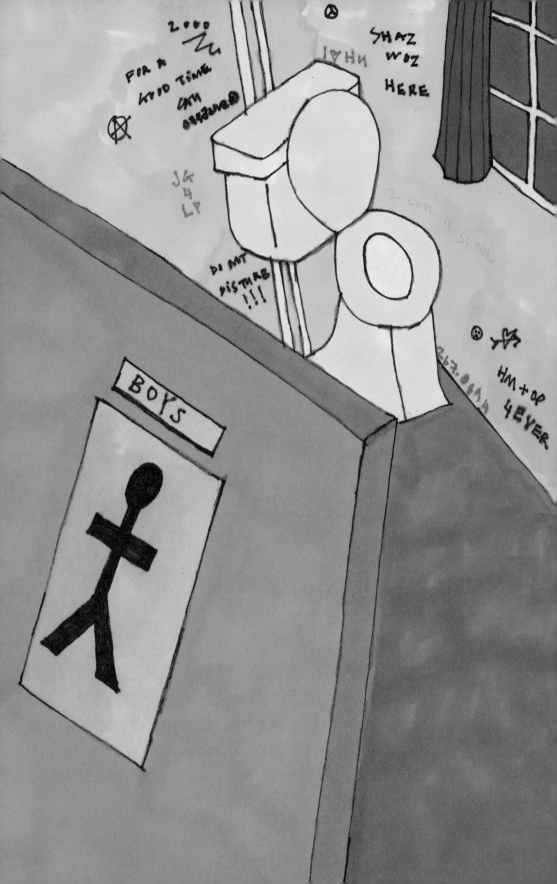

She ~~had~~ has a heart of steel.

completely no sense of other
peoples feelings.

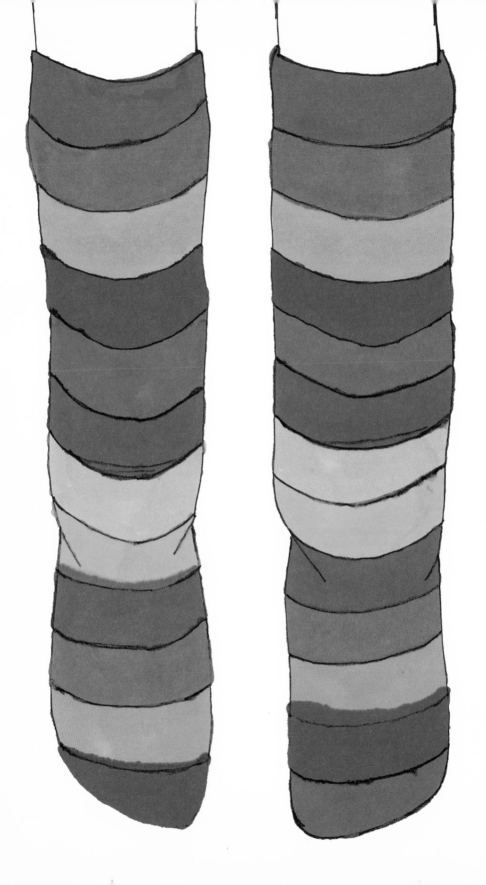

I tell her that I'm sensitive
and she says, "I'm sensitive.
I'm sensitive.I'm sensitive.
Get over it. Pull your socks
up".

When I saw her I noticed that
her lipstick was all smudged.
She asked if she could borrow
mine to re-apply.

Wow, he must like being with
someone who pulls continuous
tantrums, is super needy and
acts like a total brat! I
guess this is what's meant
by the term 'a psycho girlfriend'.

I think she's been taking
Stupid pills again.

You wouldn't think that
your so called best friend
who is married with a child
would pounce on the guy that
you've been sleeping with,
then state that it was okay
'coz "you weren't together".

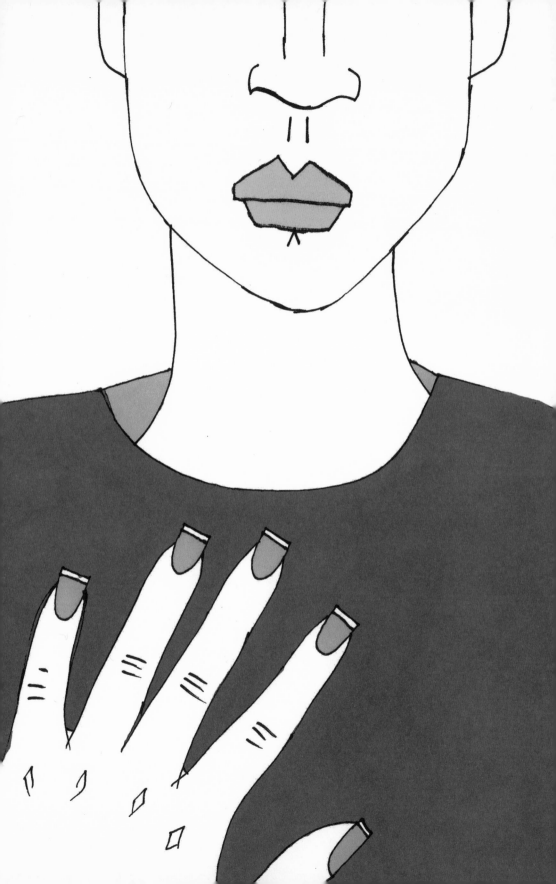

At the moment she doesn't
pick up the phone when I

call 'coz she has caller ID,
sees my name and doesn't

want to answer. She owes me

money and can't deal with
responsibility.

She gives me a permanent
anxiety attack.

What really bugged me about
her was that whenever she
was over at my house she
would rummage through my

medicine cabinet and use
all my beauty products.
Especially my expensive

moisturising creams that
I'd purchased at Fred Segals
in L.A. (that were so much

cheaper there than here in

London).

Or maybe it was that she'd
squeeze into one of my old
dresses and say that she
'had ꟿ to wear it' to the
wedding she was attending
as 'it e would be perfect'!
Funny how she seemed to be
that little bit bigger than
me (2 dress sizes). She
returned the dress but
failed to mention that
she had ripped it while
out and about. I could see
that it had been torn
from the invisible thread
that was holding it
together.

Rarely do I freak out, but
this one time I do. I tell her
that I don't want to see
her again and 'not to call
me', because she's so ~~inte~~
intense, such a nuisance,
busybody, pest, weirdo,
insane, annoying and utterly
crazy. She calls regardless.
I am completely sincere
when I say I can't deal
with her. What part of that
does she not understand?

I told her that my date had
stood me up. She said, 'well
obviously he got a better

offer!'

I ~~ded~~ decided to bring a new
friend to lunch with me, someone my old girl friend hadn't
met before (and not knowing
her step-mother would be there
During ~~li~~ lunch my old friend
turned to me and said, "Who

is this obnoxious girl you
brought along?"

Her goody two shoes routine

~~mad~~   makes me sick.

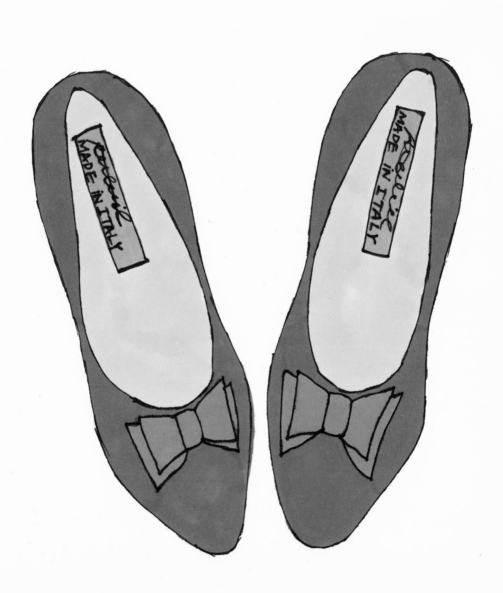

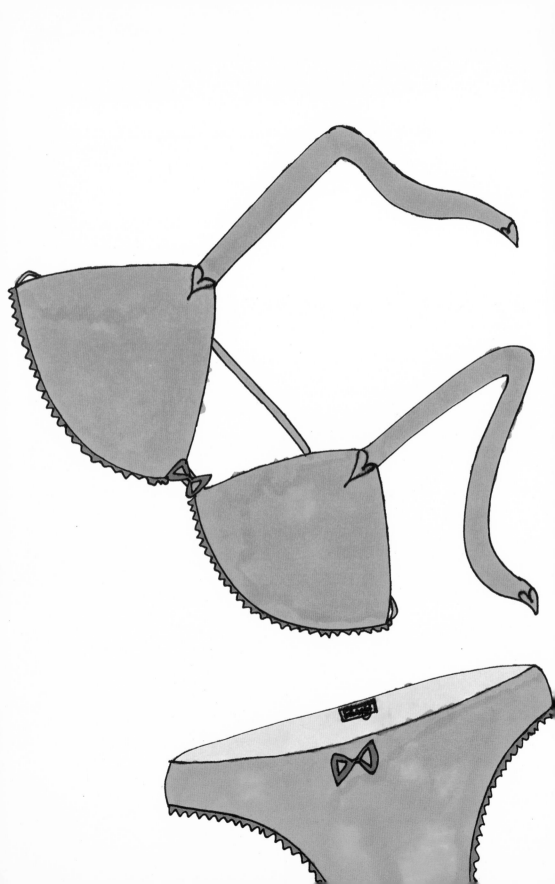

When we meet up she tells
me that she got together
with him. In a very blasé
tone she says, "he told me
he didn't want to be with
you".

Memo:

New Year's Resolution

I need to leave out all destructive people from my life. I know who they are and I need to stop spending time with them. I always feel so guilty, but I shouldn't. I can't be friends with everyone! I'm so over so many people that I don't need to waste my time anymore. I can't be friends with someone who doesn't respect me, even if they say they do. I want someone to appreciate me, not be condescending towards me which I feel constantly.

I decide ᴘ to take some action
and go see Dr.Stein, a
therapist based in North
London...

£8o later and he hadn't
really told me anything I
didn't already know...
"If you feel their energy
is negative, it may help
to edit some people out
of your life; with others
it's not so easy as you
have a history with them.

People can bring good and
bad feelings into one's
life," he said.

TELEPHONE NUMBERS & ADDRESSES
A B C D E F G H I J K L M N O P Q R S T U V W X Y Z
Notes
1 2 3 4 5 6 7 9 0
REDIAL

Sometimes I think that I
should change my telephone
number. But why? She would
just be able to find the
new number from someone
else! Plus I'd have to
give everyone my new
number and that would be
such a bore. Maybe I should
block her number next time
she ~~eak~~ calls, with any
~~li~~ luck she may get the
hint?

She called me and said,'I'm
not supposed to tell you this
but I thought you should know
that I think he's going out
with her and apparently he's

stayed at her house everyday

this week.' In this really
condescending voice she kept
saying, "Are you depressed?"

She should think before she
speaks!

When I last saw her she was
like, "I love you", as if
that term of endearment is
supposed to ~~she~~ change
everything. Like I'm going
to forgive her. I don't
think she even realises
she's done anything wrong.

the

end

About the Book

In 'I Told You So', Daisy de Villeneuve
continues her diaristic exploration of
the everyday drama of urban friendship and love. Outwardly mundane
tales of relationships and romance,
as experienced by contemporary
young women, have emerged strongly
in recent years as material for artists
working in many forms. Previously
the preserve of agony columns, soaps
and girls or women's magazines, these
subjects now inform not only adult
comics by the likes of Julie Doucet
and zines such as Cheap Date, but
also figure in the work of prominent
visual artists like Tracy Emin and
Georgina Starr. Nor is the phenomenon
confined to the work of women artists,
as the success of Daniel Clowes' Ghost
World demonstrates. Daisy has in
common with many of these artists
a talent for understated but acute
personal/social observation and a
finely tuned sense of deadpan irony.

The world which unfolds in this new
book is similar to that visited in Daisy's
previous book. But the bittersweet
aftertaste that inflected the romantic
ambiguities of that collection develops
here into something decidedly, and
entertainingly, darker. One of the
strengths of Daisy's work is her use
of repetition – her ability as an artist
to play the same phrase (or reiterate
the same idea) over and over again in
slightly different guises, as parts of a
larger work – here a story which
unfolds in closely related fragments.

'I Told You So' is a work which is both repetitive in form and which takes a form of repetition as its subject: the narrator's inability to avoid constantly falling into the same trap. Daisy has replaced the stringing together of laconic, and apparently unrelated, vignettes that characterised earlier work with a more focussed and character-driven narrative of sorts. Except that the main character of 'I Told You So' is not really a person, more a monstrous female type, a nemesis conjured from the depths of teenage agony pages, photo novels and, if we are to take the opening lines of the tale at face value, Daisy's own experience.

This recurring 'she' (we never get to know their names) is the best friend from hell, a ruthless and unhinged bitch-archetype who keeps morphing and reincarnating throughout a girl's life. And more to the point for the reader perhaps - who specifically are these girls? Daisy gives little away – yet the archnaivety of her words and drawings at the same time underscores the aching familiarity of the people and scenarios she depicts. The more one reads, the more the question of the basis of these girls in de Villeneuve's personal, 'diaristic' reality fades into irrelevance. 'I Told You So' is the story of an abstract, archetypal opponent who few girls could fail to recognise – the doppelganger who steals into her life and her mind, turns it upside down and won't let go.

The Artist as Wonderwoman

The Artist as Artist

The Author

Daisy de Villeneuve arrived on the London illustration scene catching the attention of journalists and art directors through the cult book "He said, She Said". Born in 1975 and conceived to the pop song "Kung Fu Fighting", she was brought up around the world of fashion: her mother Jan a model and her father Justin a photographer. She has exhibited her work in New York, London, Tokyo, Zurich and Hydra.

The Typewriter

The text of this book was written with a second hand Olympia, model number 784345, made in 1947 and bought by the author at Squires' Antiques in Kent fifty-six years later. The original advertisment assured us that this typewriter was "the next generation of quality and precision."

Swans fall in Love and

remain partners until

Death.